Kim Woodworth

11.19.08

TODAYICAN PUBLISHING, 2008

today I can
Say Anything

By Kim Woodworth
Illustrated by Alexis Gastwirth

For Hunter and Ben, who can say ANYTHING!

Today I can say anything!

**Today I'll say dark
when I should say light**

**Today I'll say down
when I should say up**

**Today I'll say kitty
when I should say pup**

Today I can say anything!

Today I'll say coat
when I should say hat

Today I'll say ball
when I should say bat

I'll be silly and funny
as long as I'm nice

I'll say anything,
I may say it twice!

HELLO
HELLO

KITE
KITE

STAR
STAR

JUMP
JUMP

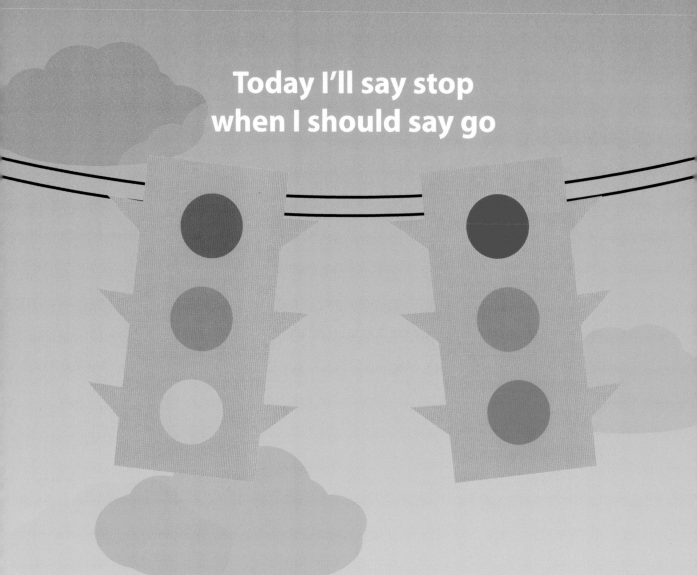

Today I'll say stop
when I should say go

Today I'll say finger
when I should say toe

Today I can say anything – wherever I go!

Today I'll say close
when I should say far

I'll be silly and funny
with a mischevious grin

What would you like to say today?